HSE

BLACKPOOL A
IE FYLDE COLL

D0765925

Introduction to

ASBESTOS
ESSENTIALS

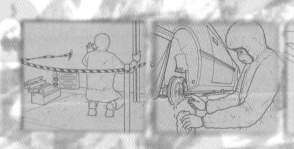

ESSENTIALS ASBESTOS

omprehensive g   with asbestos
in the building   llied trades

HSE BOOKS

© *Crown copyright 2001*
Applications for reproduction should be made in writing to:
Copyright Unit, Her Majesty's Stationery Office,
St Clements House, 2-16 Colegate, Norwich NR3 1BQ

First published 2001
Reprinted 2001

ISBN 0 7176 1901 X

This guidance is issued by the Health and Safety Executive.
Following the guidance is not compulsory and you are free to
take other action. But if you do follow the guidance you will
normally be doing enough to comply with the law. Health and
safety inspectors seek to secure compliance with the law and
may refer to this guidance as illustrating good practice.

CONTENTS

ASBESTOS BUILDING

TYPICAL LOCATIONS FOR THE MOST COMMON
ASBESTOS-CONTAINING MATERIALS

KEY

ROOF AND EXTERIOR WALLS

1. Roof sheets and tiles
2. Guttering and drainpipe
3. Wall cladding
4. Soffit boards
5. Panel beneath window
6. Roofing felt and coating to metal wall cladding

BOILER, VESSELS AND PIPEWORK

7. Lagging on boiler, pipework, calorifier etc.
8. Damaged lagging and associated debris
9. Paper lining under non-asbestos pipe lagging
10. Gasket in pipe and vessel joints
11. Rope seal on boiler access hatch and between cast iron boiler sections
12. Paper lining inside steel boiler casing
13. Boiler flue

CEILINGS

14. Spray coating to ceiling, walls, beams/columns
15. Loose asbestos in ceiling/floor cavity
16. Tiles, slats, canopies and firebreaks above ceilings
17. Textured coatings and paints

INTERIOR WALLS/PANELS

18. Loose asbestos inside partition walls
19. Partition walls
20. Panel beneath window
21. Panel lining to lift shaft
22. Panelling to vertical and horizontal beams
23. Panel behind electrical equipment
24. Panel on access hatch to service riser
25. Panel lining service riser and floor
26. Heater cupboard around domestic boiler
27. Panel behind/under heater
28. Panel on or inside, fire door
29. Bath panel

FLOORING MATERIALS

30. Floor tiles, linoleum and paper backing, lining to suspended floor

AIR HANDLING SYSTEMS

31. Lagging
32. Gaskets
33. Anit-vibration gaiter

DOMESTIC APPLIANCES

34. Gaskets, rope seals and panels in domestic boilers
35. 'Caposil' insulating blocks, panels, paper, string etc in domestic heater
36. String seals on radiators

OTHER

37. Fire blanket
38. Water tank
39. Brake/clutch lining

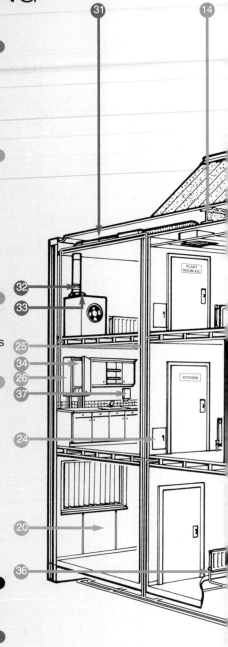

Note: This diagram does not show all possible uses and locations of asbestos-containing materials. A detailed survey will be required to identify all asbestos-containing materials present in a building.

Further information can be found in the HSE publication MDHS100 *Surveying, sampling and assessment of asbestos-containing materials*[8]

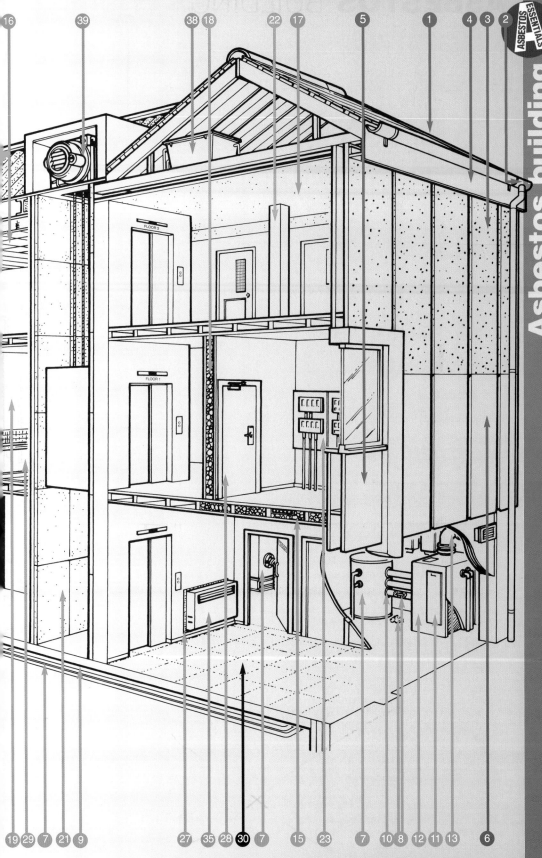

Asbestos building

v

PREFACE

Asbestos was the main cause of occupational ill health in the second half of the twentieth century. The legacy from high exposures until the 1970s is now responsible for between 2000 and 3000 people dying from asbestos-related cancers every year.

These deaths are tragic for the people involved and cause pain and suffering to relatives, friends and colleagues. They also cost the country money. If the proper management procedures had been in place and the correct work practices used by well-trained and equipped workers, most of these deaths could have been avoided.

To ensure that high levels of exposure do not occur during work on asbestos-containing materials (ACMs), HSE has put in place a rigorous regulatory and licensing regime, backed up by comprehensive practical guidance. This guidance adds to the scheme by providing guidance on maintenance work with ACMs which does not fall under the Asbestos (Licensing) Regulations 1983 (as amended).

REMEMBER

Using this guidance can help prevent you or your employees joining those who have died from an asbestos-related disease.

You can get further advice from the British Institute of Occupational Hygienists (BIOH) Tel: 01332 298087; Asbestos Testing and Consultancy (ATAC) who are a division of the Asbestos Removal Contractors Association (ARCA) Tel: 01283 531126; the Asbestos Control and Abatement Division (ACAD) Tel: 01325 466704; your trade association or HSE's InfoLine: Tel: 08701 545500.

INTRODUCTION

WHO NEEDS TO USE THIS GUIDANCE?

1   This guidance is aimed at anyone who is liable to control or carry out maintenance work with asbestos-containing materials (ACMs) which does not require a licence from HSE.

REMEMBER

Work with any type of ACM is potentially dangerous.

If you have any doubts that you or your employees can carry out the work safely, employ a specialist contractor licensed by HSE.

You can get details of licensed asbestos removal contractors from HSE's InfoLine Tel: 08701 545500.

2 This guidance will be particularly useful to employers, contract managers, site agents, safety representatives and self-employed contractors involved in maintaining buildings and associated plant. Examples of the wide range of trades where workers may come across ACMs during their normal day-to-day work (not in order of risk) include:

- ◆ demolition contractors;
- ◆ roofing contractors;
- ◆ construction contractors;
- ◆ heating and ventilation engineers;
- ◆ telecommunications engineers;
- ◆ fire and burglar alarm installers;
- ◆ general maintenance staff;
- ◆ computer installers;
- ◆ building surveyors.

- ◆ electricians;
- ◆ painters and decorators;
- ◆ joiners;
- ◆ plumbers;
- ◆ gas fitters;
- ◆ plasterers;
- ◆ builders;
- ◆ shop fitters;

The practical guidance given in the separate publication, *Asbestos essentials: Task manual*[1] will be of particular use to employees who carry out maintenance work on ACMs.

3   *This list is by no means exhaustive.* If your trade is not included, it *does not* mean that you or your employees are not in danger. The list illustrates that asbestos was used widely. Anyone whose work causes disturbance to the fabric of a building or plant may be at risk of exposure to asbestos.

WHY IS THIS GUIDANCE NEEDED?

4   In 1995 an influential scientific paper[2] identified the largest group of workers currently at risk from exposure to asbestos fibres (see paragraph 2-3). Workers in these and similar trades may encounter asbestos during their normal day-to-day work.

5   This research showed that 2000-3000 people are dying each year from asbestos-related diseases, in particular mesothelioma (see paragraph 20). About a quarter of these deaths are in the types of trades listed in paragraph 2.

Figure 1 Asbestos paper lining

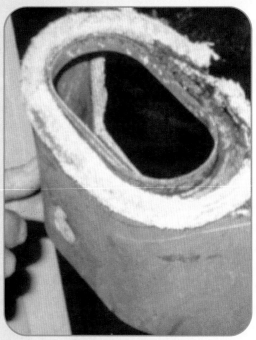

Figure 2 Asbestos rope seal

6   These deaths are mainly due to high exposures to asbestos before today's Regulations were introduced. However, these trades can still come across ACMs and may have to work on them. For example, Figures 1 and 2 show typical ACMs you may find when carrying out maintenance work in a building.

7   The type of work you can carry out is restricted by the Asbestos (Licensing) Regulations 1983 (as amended) (see paragraphs 37-41).

8   Exposure to asbestos fibres can occur when ACMs are not identified before work is started or when the work is badly planned. Table 1 gives some examples of the exposures which can occur during a range of tasks. Compare these with the control limits in Table 2 (see also paragraphs 33-36).

Table 1 Typical exposures to asbestos fibres, where poor control measures and work practices have been used (fibres per millilitre of air (f/ml))

Task	Typical exposure (f/ml)
Dry removal of sprayed (limpet) coating	up to 1000
Dry removal of lagging	up to 100
Drilling AIB	up to 10
Use of a jigsaw on AIB	up to 20
Hand sawing AIB	up to 10
Sweeping AIB debris	up to 100
Drilling AC	up to 1
Hand sawing AC	up to 1
Use of a circular saw on AC	up to 20

AIB: Asbestos insulating board
AC: Asbestos cement

REASONABLY PRACTICABLE

Reducing exposure 'so far as reasonably practicable' means that: you must reduce exposure to the point where there is a big difference between, on the one hand, the sacrifice (in money, time or trouble) that would be involved in further measures and, on the other hand, the risks from exposure (which should be insignificant).

9   If ACMs are identified and the work is planned and carried out using the proper precautions, exposure can either be prevented or reduced to a level that is as low as *reasonably practicable*.

10   Put simply, people will not be exposed to asbestos fibres unless the material is disturbed, making the fibres airborne. But, any activity which disturbs an ACM can, if not controlled, result in exposure of workers to asbestos fibres.

11   Figure 3 shows a piece of asbestos lagging being *gently* shaken. Note the cloud of dust above the lagging. This will contain a large number of microscopic asbestos fibres. This illustrates how easily fibres can be made airborne (the potential to release fibres varies with the type of ACM and the task being carried out - see paragraphs 54-58).

Figure 3 A piece of asbestos lagging being gently shaken

HOW TO USE THIS GUIDANCE

12   This guidance takes you through a number of steps to help you prevent or, where this is not reasonably practicable, control exposure to asbestos (Figure 4). It first helps you decide if you have a problem (for example are ACMs present?) and what to do about it.

13   It then provides practical general advice on good work practices and the type of equipment needed, for example a Type H vacuum cleaner. This information is supported by *Asbestos essentials: Task manual*[1] which explains how to carry out common tasks safely. This publication is explained in more detail in paragraphs 174-179.

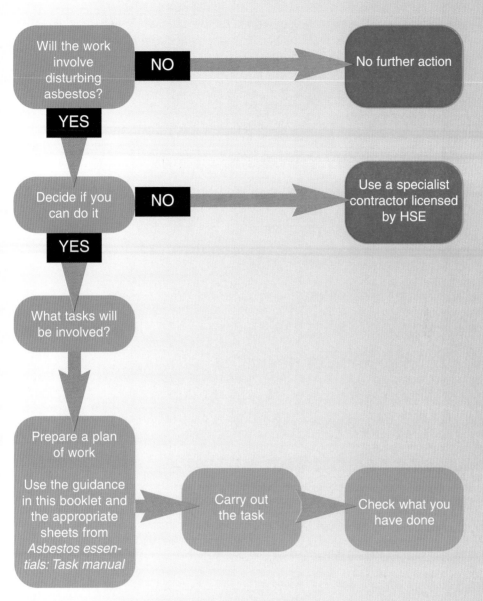

Figure 4 A stepwise approach to using this guidance

14   General guidance on safe working with asbestos cement is
given in *Working with asbestos cement*.[3] Guidance on carrying
out specific tasks with asbestos cement is given in the task guidance sheets, A9-A16.[1]

WHAT IS ASBESTOS?

15   Asbestos is a term used for the fibrous forms of several naturally occurring minerals.

16 The three main types of asbestos which have been commercially used are:

◆ crocidolite (often referred to as 'blue asbestos');

◆ amosite (often referred to as 'brown asbestos');

◆ chrysotile (often referred to as 'white asbestos').

(Figure 5 shows bundles of microscopic brown (amosite) asbestos fibres. These would not be visible to the naked eye.)

17   *All are dangerous,* but blue and brown asbestos are known to be more dangerous than white. *The different types cannot usually be identified by their colour alone.*

18   Where asbestos is affected by heat or chemicals, or combined with other substances, the colour and appearance can change.

Figure 5 Bundles of microscopic brown asbestos fibres

19   There is no simple test to identify the different types of asbestos. Laboratory analysis is required. They often occur as mixtures and unless you are sure which type of asbestos fibres are present you must treat the material as if it contains blue or brown.

HOW CAN ASBESTOS AFFECT YOU?

20   Breathing in asbestos fibres can lead to people developing one of three *fatal* diseases:

◆ *asbestosis* which is a scarring of the lung;

◆ *lung cancer;*

◆ *mesothelioma* which is a cancer of the lining around the lungs and stomach.

21   These diseases can take from 15-60 years to develop, from first exposure - so you or your employees would not be aware of any sudden change in health after breathing in asbestos.

> **REMEMBER**
>
> It is the precautions you take now which will affect your, or your employees', health in the future.

22   In general, the likelihood that people may develop one of these diseases will increase with:

◆ the type of asbestos fibre they are exposed to (blue and brown asbestos are more dangerous than white);

◆ the younger they are when exposure starts;

◆ the number of fibres they breathe in;

◆ the number of times they are exposed;

◆ smoking.

23   Asbestos fibres enter your body when you breathe. The body can get rid of the larger fibres, but microscopic fibres can pass into the lungs where they can cause disease. They can stay there for many years.

24   It is because fibres can remain in the lungs for so long that small, but repeated, exposures on different jobs over the years can lead to the development of an asbestos-related disease. *This is why it is important to prevent or control exposure on every single job.*

25　The body naturally gets rid of any asbestos fibres taken in with food and water. Asbestos fibres cannot be absorbed through the skin.

26　It is important to remember that people *who smoke and are exposed to asbestos fibres* are at greater risk of developing lung cancer than those who do not smoke. If you smoke and carry out maintenance work on ACMs, consider giving up.

27　The best way to make sure that you or your employees do not develop one of these diseases is to avoid disturbing ACMs, or, where this is unavoidable, to keep exposures as low as reasonably practicable.

WHERE CAN YOU FIND ASBESTOS?

28   ACMs have been put to many uses over the past century. A drawing of an 'asbestos building' is given on the inside front cover. This shows typical locations for the most commonly used ACMs. *Note, it does not include all the possible uses for ACMs you may come across.*

29   The commercial use of asbestos in the UK began around the end of the nineteenth century and increased gradually until World War II. Immediately after World War II, large quantities of asbestos were used, particularly for new 'system-built' buildings in the 1950s, 1960s and early 1970s. ACMs were routinely used in the refurbishment of older buildings.

30   Asbestos has been the subject of gradual voluntary and formal bans since 1969. By 1999 the importation, supply and use of all forms of ACMs had been banned (see paragraphs 42-45).

31   Figures 6-27 show some of the most common types of ACMs which you can come across in a building.

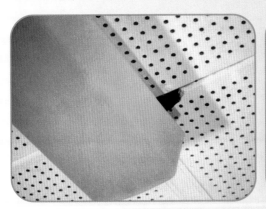

Figure 6 Perforated AIB ceiling tiles

Figure 7 Asbestos cement roof

Figure 8 Window sill reinforced with asbestos

Figure 9 Asbestos fire blanket

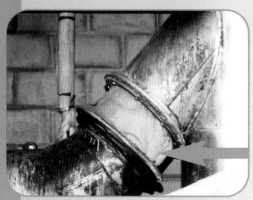

Figure 10 Flexible asbestos duct connector (gaiter)

Figure 11 Metal/asbestos flue pipe - the asbestos is between the inner and outer layers of stainless steel

Figure 12 Asbestos cement tank

Figure 13 Built-up bituminous roofing containing asbestos

Figure 14 Decorative coating containing asbestos

Figure 15 Asbestos cement drainpipe

Figure 16 Sanitary wear incinerator – the opening can be backed with an asbestos cement panel. The flue can also be made of asbestos cement

Figure 17 Asbestos cement flue - external

Figure 18 Domestic hot water cylinder lagged with asbestos

Figure 19 Domestic hot water cylinder with asbestos removed, lagged with a non-asbestos jacket

Figure 20 The same cylinder as Figure 19. Note the asbestos debris from a previous poor removal job

Figure 21 Asbestos rope seal and soft panelling on the burner/heat exchanger of a domestic boiler

Figure 22 Debris from an asbestos gasket on a pipe flange

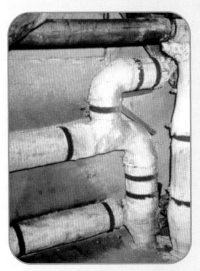

Figure 23 Asbestos pipe lagging

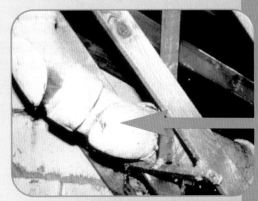

Figure 24 Asbestos cement flue in a ceiling void

Figure 25 Sectional 'caposite'
asbestos pipe lagging

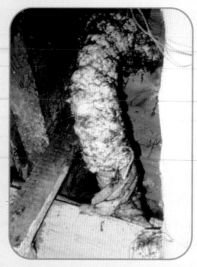

Figure 26 Asbestos rope
pipe lagging

Figure 27 Sprayed 'limpet'
coating which
has been partly removed

WHAT THE LAW REQUIRES

CONTROL OF ASBESTOS AT WORK REGULATIONS 1987 (AS AMENDED) (THE CAW REGULATIONS)

32   These Regulations require employers or the self-employed to prevent exposure to asbestos, or, where this is not reasonably practicable, to make sure that it is kept as low as reasonably practicable, and in any case below the control limit (see paragraphs 33-36).

> **REMEMBER**
>
> These Regulations apply to work with *all types* of ACMs and place duties on both employers and the self-employed.

33   The CAW Regulations give control limits for the different types of asbestos fibre. A control limit is a maximum concentration of asbestos fibres in the air (averaged over any continuous four-hour or ten-minute period). Employees must not be exposed above this level and exposure should be reduced as low as reasonably practicable below the control limit. This must be achieved by measures other than respiratory protective equipment (RPE), for example by using the methods given in *Asbestos essentials: Task manual.*[1] Where this cannot be achieved, RPE must be worn to reduce exposure as low as reasonably practicable and in any case below the control limit.

34   Both the four-hour and ten-minute periods have their own control limits, the values of which vary depending on the type of asbestos present. The control limits are given in Table 2.

35   Action levels apply to exposure in the longer term, and are cumulative exposures calculated over any continuous twelve-week period. The twelve-week period should not be chosen in such a way as to avoid exceeding an action level; it should represent a 'worst-case' for the work being undertaken. The action levels are given in Table 2.

Table 2 Control limits and action levels for asbestos

Asbestos type	4-hour control limit (f/ml)	10-minute control limit (f/ml)	Action level (fibre hrs/ml)
White asbestos alone	0.3	0.9	72
Any other form of asbestos, either alone or in mixtures, including mixtures of white asbestos with any other form of asbestos	0.2	0.6	48

36   If an action level is exceeded you will need to comply with a number of additional regulations within the CAW Regulations. You will need to:

◆ notify the enforcing authority responsible for the site where you are working (for example HSE or the Local Authority);

◆ designate the work area (see paragraphs 113-121);

◆ pay for your employees to undergo medical surveillance.

Further information can be found in the Approved Code of Practice, *Control of Asbestos at Work Regulations.*[4]

THE ASBESTOS (LICENSING) REGULATIONS 1983 (AS AMENDED)

37   Under these Regulations, anyone carrying out work on asbestos insulation, asbestos coating or asbestos insulating board (AIB) will need a licence issued by HSE *(this includes work on the ACM and subsequent cleaning of any contaminated dust or debris)*. The exceptions to these requirements are:

◆ when a person does not work with asbestos insulation, asbestos coating or AIB for more than one hour in seven consecutive days (this is all jobs within the seven days) and the total time spent on that work by all employees does not exceed two hours;

Figure 28 An office made from AIB

◆ when the work is carried out on your own premises using your own specially trained and equipped employees. Although you must still give formal notification (14 days) of such work to the relevant enforcing authority, for example HSE.

◆ when the work is limited to air monitoring (see paragraphs 160-166) or the collection of bulk samples to identify whether asbestos is present;

◆ clearance testing (see paragraphs 155-159).

38   It is important that the amount of time you or your employees spend working with asbestos insulation, asbestos coatings or AIB is managed to make sure that they do not exceed the time limits given in paragraph 37.

39   Figure 28 shows an office built from AIB inside a warehouse. If you wanted to demolish the office you would exceed the time limits given in paragraph 37. The job would need to be carried out by a specialist contractor licensed by HSE. But, you would be able to drill holes in the wall to pass a wire through, as long as the time limits were not exceeded. Or, you could remove a single screwed-in piece of AIB (see A1 'Drilling holes in asbestos insulating board' and A4 'Removal of a single screwed-in asbestos insulating board less than 2m^2 in area' respectively).[1]

40   Work on the following materials is also outside these Regulations:

◆ asbestos cement;

◆ articles made of rubber, plastic, resin or bitumen which contain asbestos, for example vinyl floor tiles, electric cables and roofing felt;

◆ other insulation products which may be used at high temperatures but have no insulation purposes, for example gaskets, washers, ropes and seals.

REMEMBER

You will need to include time spent building a mini-enclosure or carrying out final clearing work in your time estimate (see paragraph 37).

Although you may not need a licence to carry out a particular job you will still need to comply with the requirements of the CAW Regulations.

41   Further information can be found in the flow chart in Figure 41 and the HSE publication, *A guide to the Asbestos (Licensing) Regulations.*[5]

ASBESTOS (PROHIBITIONS) REGULATIONS 1992 (AS AMENDED)

42   These Regulations prohibit the importation, supply and use of all forms of asbestos. Blue and brown asbestos were banned in 1985 and the remaining uses of white asbestos banned in 1999. It is therefore illegal to import, supply or use raw asbestos or new products containing it, and to supply or use existing products for a new purpose. Products in use before the date the Regulations came into force can continue to be used until such time as they need to be replaced. The Regulations also specifically ban the use of second-hand asbestos cement products, and of second-hand boards, tiles or panels which have been painted or covered with paint or textured plaster containing asbestos.

43   The 1999 Prohibitions Amendment Regulations permit the continued use of white asbestos for a limited period in a few specialised areas, where there is no suitable substitute available. With one exception, all new uses of asbestos will have ceased by January 2005.

Figure 29 Asbestos rope seal in a domestic boiler

44   Figure 29 shows an asbestos rope seal, containing white asbestos, between the heat exchanger and flue on a domestic boiler. This material can remain in use until the end of its service life. However, if it needs to be replaced, a suitable asbestos-free material must be used.

45   Nevertheless, it may be a good idea to remove the asbestos product if the unit has been dismantled and to replace it with a suitable non-asbestos substitute. This will prevent further exposure when the unit is next worked on.

> **REMEMBER**
>
> These Regulations apply to new uses for asbestos. ACMs may be left in place and managed.

CONSTRUCTION (DESIGN AND MANAGEMENT) REGULATIONS 1994 (CDM) AND CONSTRUCTION (HEALTH, SAFETY AND WELFARE) REGULATIONS 1996 (CHSW)

46 You must also comply with the:

◆ Construction (Design and Management) Regulations 1994 (CDM); and

◆ Construction (Health, Safety and Welfare) Regulations 1996 (CHSW).

47   Further guidance can be found in the Approved Code of Practice *Managing construction for health and safety*[6] which accompanies the CDM Regulations and the leaflet *A guide to the Construction (Health, Safety and Welfare) Regulations 1996,*[7] respectively.

MANAGING THE RISK FROM WORK WITH ASBESTOS

THE HAZARDS AND RISKS OF ACMS

48 Asbestos can cause a number of fatal lung diseases. This is what is known as the *hazard*.

49 The hazard will vary with the type of asbestos fibre in the material. *All forms of asbestos are dangerous,* but blue and brown are more dangerous than white. It is quite common for ACMs to contain a mixture of fibre types. Unless you are sure of the type of asbestos present, for example by having a representative sample analysed by a laboratory, you must treat the material as if it contains blue or brown asbestos.

50 Figure 23 shows asbestos-lagged pipework, which can contain a mixture of all three types of asbestos fibre.

51 The type of asbestos fibre used in the manufacture of different products often varied over the years, for example white asbestos was the main form used in the manufacture of asbestos cement, however, blue asbestos was used from 1950-69 and brown asbestos between 1945 to around 1980. Asbestos cement containing blue or brown asbestos would pose a greater hazard than if it contained white asbestos alone.

52 If ACMs are damaged or disturbed, fibres can get into the air more easily than if they are undamaged and undisturbed.

HAZARD

Hazard means anything that can cause harm (for example asbestos).

RISK

This is the chance, high or low, that somebody will be harmed by the hazard.

REMEMBER

If the ACMs are kept in good condition and left undisturbed, fibres will not get into the air where they can be breathed in. ACMs should only be worked on when it is absolutely necessary.

53 Once they are in the air, fibres can be breathed in. This is called exposure. The higher the exposure, the greater the *risk*. (Hazard x exposure = risk)

Managing the risk from work with asbestos

54   Exposure is influenced by the type of material in which the fibres are bound, for example, a loosely bound sprayed 'limpet' asbestos coating is more likely to release fibres when disturbed than asbestos cement where the fibres are firmly bound in the cement matrix (Figures 30 and 31).

Figure 30 Distance (left) and close up (right) pictures of sprayed 'limpet' asbestos coatings. These can contain up to 85% asbestos which is loosely bound. This type of material readily releases fibres when disturbed

Figure 31 Asbestos cement generally contains 10-15% asbestos fibre bound in a cement matrix. Because the fibres are firmly bound in the cement matrix they will only be released if the material is subject to significant disturbance, such as drilling or sawing

55   The potential for fibres to be released into the air from different ACMs can be ranked as follows:

HIGH

Sprayed coatings/loose fill

Lagging and packings

AIB

Rope and gaskets

Millboard and paper

Asbestos cement

Floor tiles, mastic and roof felt

Decorative paints and plasters

LOW

REMEMBER

REMEMBER

The fact that work is on ACMs with a lower potential to release fibres *does not* mean that it is safe. It must still be managed and the proper precautions taken.

56   The level of exposure will also depend on the task being carried out. Tasks which cause significant disturbance to the ACMs will result in more fibres being released into the air.

57   The same task carried out on different types of ACMs can result in different levels of exposure. For example, drilling AIB will result in much higher exposures than similar work on asbestos cement, as it has a higher fibre content than asbestos cement

(16-40% compared with 10-15%). Also, the fibres are more firmly bound into the matrix of the asbestos cement and therefore less likely to be made airborne. Figure 32 shows an asbestos cement flue on a domestic boiler.

58   Exposure will also depend on how the task is being carried out and the precautions you take. You can reduce exposure by taking the right precautions. Table 3 gives some examples of comparative activities with high and lower potential to cause fibres to be released.

Figure 32 Asbestos cement flue on a domestic boiler

59   The level of risk will therefore depend on a combination of:

◆ the type of asbestos fibre;

◆ the type of ACMs, for example sprayed coating, lagging, AIB, asbestos cement etc;

◆ the task being carried out;

◆ the precautions taken to prevent or control exposure.

Table 3 Examples of comparable activities with a high and lower potential to cause fibres to be released

HIGH	LOWER
Abrasive power and pneumatic tools without local exhaust ventilation (LEV)	Hand tools/use of LEV
Working on dry ACMs	Working on damp ACMs
Sweeping	Vacuuming with a Type H vacuum cleaner (BS5415) (see paragraph 124)
Wire brushing	Gentle scraping using shadow vacuuming (see paragraph 124)
Breaking AIB tiles	Unscrewing AIB tiles and removing whole

MANAGING THE RISK

60   Paragraphs 61-102 explain the steps you can take to identify whether the work you plan to carry out could present a danger to you, your employees, and others and then decide what to do about it.

61   When you are assessing a job you must consult and work with any Safety Representatives appointed under the Safety Representatives and Safety Committees Regulations 1977, or where your employees are not represented by a trade union representative, consult them on matters relating to health and safety at work in accordance with the Health and Safety (Consultation with Employees) Regulations 1996.

62   This is important, not only because it is a legal requirement, but also because your employees will often be able to provide valuable information on problems they come across when working with ACMs and how to work safely.

63   For the purposes of this guidance, managing the risk from asbestos is often very simple and a matter of common sense. By managing the risk, you are helping to prevent you or your employees becoming asbestos-related statistics.

> **REMEMBER**
>
> Asbestos does not kill people at work immediately as would, for example falling off a roof or being hit by a fork lift truck. Some cancers can take up to 60 years to develop. Once cancer has developed there is no cure and sufferers will die a painful death.
>
> What you do about this now can affect the well-being of you or your employees for decades to come. You will not see any immediate health benefits but you can be sure that you are investing in the future health of yourself and your employees.
>
> *It is vital that you get it right today, otherwise it may be too late.*

WHEN IS THE RISK GREATEST?

64   Paragraph 2 gives examples of the types of maintenance trades where the greatest number of workers are at risk from exposure to asbestos. Because of the nature of their work, workers in these and similar trades are likely to disturb the fabric of a building or plant. There is the potential for you or your employees to be exposed to asbestos fibres, because:

♦ you are working on an unfamiliar site;

♦ ACMs were not identified before the job started;

♦ ACMs were identified but the information was not given to the people doing the work;

♦ you or your employees do not know how to recognise and work safely with asbestos;

♦ you or your employees know how to work safely but you *do not* take the proper precautions.

Contractors removing a partition wall in a secure area containing a safe did not know that the void between the inner and outer partition walls was filled with loose brown (amosite) asbestos. The walls were removed and carried, unwrapped, from the fifth floor of the building to a general skip. By the time it was realised that asbestos was present they had spread contamination along the whole route, including the lift. Consultants called in to assess the extent of the contamination confirmed that asbestos debris was present and that asbestos fibres were in the air. A specialist asbestos removal contractor was called in to decontaminate the affected areas. This simple mistake led to the contractors and office workers being exposed to asbestos, disruption of the building during the decontamination and a bill for many thousands of pounds.

65   The example in the box above illustrates why it is important that management have clear procedures in place to ensure that:

◆ ACMs have been identified if you are working on your own site;

◆ information is obtained about the presence of ACMs when working on someone else's site;

◆ in both cases, this information is given to the people in control of the work and to the workers doing the job;

◆ the appropriate actions and precautions are taken;

◆ appropriate equipment is provided;

◆ adequate training is given;

◆ there is adequate supervision.

66   Otherwise, it is possible that ACMs will be unknowingly disturbed or inadequate precautions taken. This will put people's health at risk. Figure 33 shows a damaged AIB partition wall. This type of damage can happen when ACMs are not identified before work starts.

Figure 33 AIB wall panels badly damaged during poorly planned and uncontrolled work

67 Failure to have such procedures can lead to:

◆ exposure of you, your employees and others to asbestos fibres;

◆ future ill health;

◆ costly decontamination. This can be much more expensive than the cost of dealing with the asbestos in the first place;

◆ prosecution;

◆ adverse publicity for your company;

◆ compensation claims;

◆ higher insurance premiums.

case study

A school had been surveyed for ACMs. The council employed consultants to supervise the removal of asbestos lagging from ceiling voids, the boiler room and the under floor duct. However, at the same time an engineer was drilling into AIB ceiling tiles in the school foyer without using any precautions. The engineer would have been exposed to asbestos fibres, his work clothing and the immediate area contaminated with asbestos debris. This example illustrates how an otherwise well-run management system can fail simply because of a lack of communication (on behalf of the council) and of awareness about asbestos (on the side of the engineer).

WHAT SHOULD YOU DO FIRST?

68   There are five steps that you should follow when assessing the risk to yourself or your employees and deciding what to do:

STEP 1:   LOOK FOR ASBESTOS

STEP 2:   DECIDE IF THERE IS A PROBLEM

STEP 3:   DECIDE WHAT ACTION TO TAKE

STEP 4:   RECORD YOUR FINDINGS AND TAKE ACTION

STEP 5:   CHECK WHAT YOU HAVE DONE AND REVIEW YOUR ASSESSMENT

STEP 1 LOOK FOR ASBESTOS

69   If you are working on your own premises you must manage the risks from ACMs which may be present. Where you are working on someone else's premises, the employer (your client) in control of any work on those premises must manage the risks from any ACMs present on the premises.

70   The person in control of the work must inform you of the presence of ACMs during the planning of the work (if you are working on your own site you will need to determine this yourself). Do not rely on this as your only protection. You should make sure that you ask whether the area has been surveyed and what the findings were. Figure 34 shows pieces of AIB (one of the most common forms of ACM) and Figure 35 shows AIB ceiling tiles in a corridor.

Figure 34 Pieces of AIB

Figure 35: Suspended AIB ceiling tiles in a corridor

71   It is also important to remember that debris from damaged ACMs can be found near the parent material. It may also be left over from the installation of ACMs, for example, Figure 36 shows the installation of a sprayed 'limpet' asbestos coating many years ago. This method of application frequently resulted in ACM being sprayed onto surrounding areas.

72   Debris can be easily disturbed by people working in an area. So, exposure can occur even if the task does not directly involve work on ACMs. This debris will normally need to be removed.

Figure 36 Installing a sprayed 'limpet' coating

73   Figure 37 shows an electrical switch box, next to a machine which had been used to make bituminous roofing felt containing asbestos. Wet white asbestos had 'splattered' the switch box. Although there were no ACMs nearby, anyone working on the box could be exposed to the material if it was disturbed after it had dried out.

Figure 37 Asbestos debris on an electrical box, adjacent to a machine which was used to make bituminous roofing felt containing asbestos

74   Figure 38 shows a piece of debris from a sprayed 'limpet' asbestos coating (brown asbestos) on a cable tray.

Figure 38 Asbestos debris in a cable tray

75   If the area has not been surveyed, work should not start until a survey has been carried out to check for the presence of ACMs. Further information on carrying out surveys can be found in *Surveying, sampling and assessment of asbestos-containing materials.*[8] Specialist advice can be obtained from the organisations listed on page vii.

REMEMBER

REMEMBER

DON'T FORGET TO ASK:
'Has this area been checked for ACMs?'

76   If there are no ACMs in the area where you plan to carry out the work, there is no need to take any further action as far as asbestos is concerned. However, there may be other hazards, such as working at heights, which you will need to address.

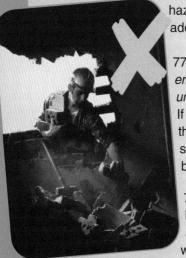

77   *However, it is important that you and your employees are aware that it is possible for ACMs to be uncovered during the course of the job* (see Figure 39). If you suspect that any material contains asbestos, even if the area has previously been declared 'asbestos-free' you should **stop work** until the material has been investigated by a competent person (see paragraphs 126-128).

78   Figure 40 shows a section of damaged AIB in a kitchen. This material had not been identified during the asbestos survey. It was uncovered by ventilation engineers who damaged the AIB before they realised what it was. This led to contamination of the kitchen and the exposure of the engineers and kitchen staff to asbestos fibres. Work was delayed for a day while the area was decontaminated.

Figure 39
A workman has broken through a brick wall. This disturbed a previously hidden lining of AIB.

Figure 40 Damaged AIB

79   A similar problem can occur if the scope of the work changes during the job. This could bring additional areas or equipment within its scope. Work should not take place until the asbestos register (a record of the presence of ACMs) has been consulted or the area surveyed.

REMEMBER

You and your employees should always be alert to the danger presented by *'hidden'* ACMs.

STEP 2 DECIDE IF THERE IS A PROBLEM

80   You will now know whether ACMs are present. What you now need to do is decide whether anyone is likely to be exposed to asbestos fibres and how much, as a result of the work. This is often referred to as a 'risk assessment'.

81   To do this you will need to find out what the work will involve, for example:

◆ the type and quantity of ACMs present;

◆ the condition of the ACMs (if damaged the risk may be greater);

◆ which tasks will directly disturb the ACMs, for example drilling AIB;

◆ which tasks could indirectly disturb ACMs, for example removing a door with the AIB backing panel intact;

◆ how the work will be carried out, which methods will be used to prevent or control exposure, including the use of personal protective equipment;

◆ the likely levels of exposure;

◆ how long the job will take;

◆ any other information relevant to safe working practices, for example prevention of falls.

Further information on carrying out risk assessments for work with asbestos can be found in the CAW Approved Code of Practice.[4]

82   It is also important that you find out who may be affected by your work. Don't forget that there may be other people present besides you or your employees, for example:

◆ other workers in the vicinity of the job;

◆ visitors;

◆ the public.

83   You must pay particular attention to young workers or trainees who may be at special risk because of their lack of experience.

84   If a number of jobs are very similar you need only carry out one detailed risk assessment which will cover all of them. But, you will still need to check that the jobs really are similar and that your work will not affect others. Also, if there is a change in the type of work being carried out or the way you do it then you will need to review the assessment.

85   Some of the materials you use may contain hazardous substances, for example solvents in adhesive sprays. You will need to assess exposure under the Control of Substances Hazardous to Health Regulations 1999 (COSHH). Where reasonably practicable you should use products containing the least hazardous components. Otherwise you will need to control exposure as determined by your assessment. Further information can be found in *COSHH: A brief guide to the Regulations.*[9]

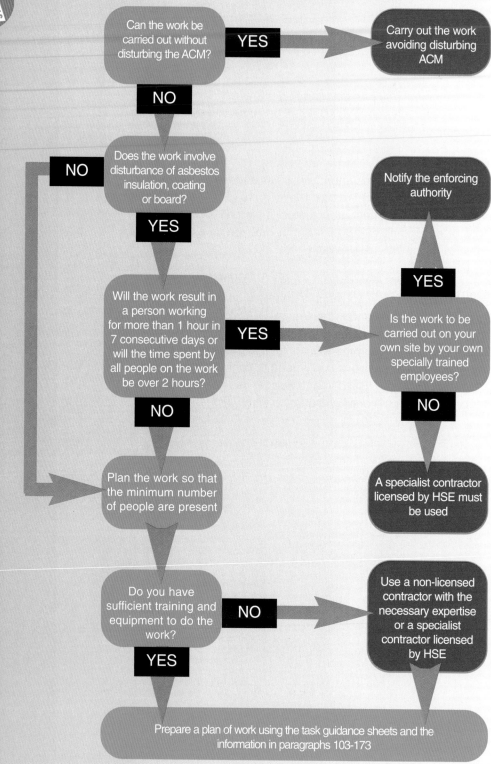

Figure 41 A simple decision flow chart. This will help you decide who should carry out the work

STEP 3 DECIDE WHAT ACTION TO TAKE

86   Using the information collected in Steps 1 and 2, you can take one of three decisions (Figure 41):

◆ the work must be carried out by a specialist contractor licensed by HSE;

◆ the work can be carried out without a licence but someone with more expertise, appropriate equipment etc than yourself is needed to do it;

◆ the work can be carried out without a licence and you have adequate training and equipment to do it safely.

87   If you can, and choose to carry out the work yourself, you should:

◆ where reasonably practicable, plan the work so that ACMs are not disturbed;

◆ develop a safe system of work. You can do this by using the general advice given in paragraphs 103-173 and then choosing the appropriate guidance sheets from *Asbestos essentials: Task manual*,[1] for example, Figure 42 shows attachments which can be used when drilling small and large holes in AIB; Figure 43 shows one in use (EM4 'Using a Type H vacuum cleaner when working with asbestos' and A1 'Drilling holes in asbestos insulating board' respectively).[1] This will form the basis of the plan of work for the job.

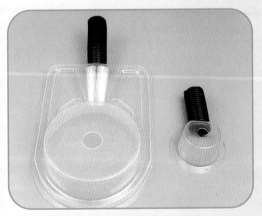

Figure 42 A plastic 'enclosure' for use when drilling AIB

Figure 43 A plastic 'enclosure' in use

88 The plan of work should include:

◆ the nature and likely duration of the work;

◆ the address and location of the work;

◆ when the work should be carried out;

◆ the work procedures and precautions to be taken to reduce exposure to as low as reasonably practicable and prevent the spread of asbestos, for example, Figure 44 shows LEV being used when unscrewing AIB;

◆ the equipment required, including personal protective equipment;

◆ decontamination;

◆ emergency procedures;

Figure 44 Using LEV during unscrewing AIB

◆ whether replacement non-ACMs are required;

◆ the level of supervision required. This will vary with the nature and extent of the work.

> REMEMBER
>
> ◆ Your first aim should be to prevent exposure.
>
> ◆ Where this not possible you should reduce exposure as far as reasonably practicable.

89   The plan of work and *Asbestos essentials: Task manual*[1] should be issued to the workers carrying out the tasks. The task manual contains task guidance sheets and the equipment and method guidance sheets (see paragraphs 174-179). It is important that the correct task guidance sheets are used. It is not good enough to use a 'similar' one.

REMEMBER

It is important that the workers carrying out the procedures in the plan of work understand it and have received adequate training.

90   It is no good producing a safe plan of work if you do not provide your employees with the tools to do the job. The equipment you provide should be appropriate for the job, clean and in good working order.

91   Although site conditions can change, the jobs/tasks that people carry out may be similar. Consequently, it can be possible to prepare generic plans of work. These would only require minor modification to highlight where ACMs can be found and any other specific requirements of the site.

92   A copy of the assessment and plan of work should be kept readily available at the work site and be followed. If there is a need to modify the plan of work, this should be agreed with the site supervisor or client.

Finally - you should ask yourself:

'Have I done all that I can to prevent or reduce exposure to asbestos fibres?'

STEP 4 RECORD YOUR FINDINGS AND TAKE ACTION

93   You need to make sure that everyone involved in the work is fully aware of the plan of work and why each action is being taken. They should also be properly equipped for, and trained in, the procedures laid down in the plan of work.

94   If you have fewer than five employers you do not have to record the findings of your assessment, but it is useful to do so. If you employ more than five employees, the Management of Health and Safety at Work Regulations 1999 requires you to record the significant findings of your assessment.[10]

STEP 5 CHECK WHAT YOU HAVE DONE AND REVIEW YOUR ASSESSMENT

95   Good management is an ongoing process. Where the type of work changes you will need to repeat steps 1 to 4 to decide whether the risk has changed and if you will need to modify the plan of work.

96   You will also need to ensure that the systems that you have put in place to prevent or control the risk are being used correctly and are effective. The type of work covered in this guidance may be carried out anywhere on your site, or, if you are a contractor, on the site of your client.

97   It is therefore important that you have an effective system of supervision. This can range from a supervisor on a particular job to a safety advisor who can visit the site/job unannounced.

98   If you are self-employed, you will normally not have anyone who will check that you are working correctly. Because of this, it is important that you familiarise yourself fully with the advice given in this guidance and follow it closely.

99 To ensure that the measures you have taken are continuing to be effective you can make the following checks:

◆ make sure that everyone is following the plan of work;

◆ where necessary, monitor your employees' exposure to asbestos fibres (see paragraphs 160-166);

◆ regularly review your assessment of exposure;

◆ routinely clean, inspect and test all equipment;

◆ provide your employees with refresher training at appropriate intervals (see paragraphs 109-111).

REMEMBER

Good management will anticipate problems rather than deal with them after they have occurred.

Work with any type of ACM is potentially dangerous.

If you have any doubts about how to carry out the work safely it is recommended that you consider employing a specialist contractor licensed by HSE.

EMERGENCY CALL-OUT PROCEDURES

100   Wherever possible, work with asbestos should be carefully planned in advance. However, there will be situations where it may not be possible to prepare a specific assessment and plan of work, for example, a burst pipe behind an AIB panel in a department store at night.

101   This does not mean that you or your employees can cut corners.

REMEMBER

It is in situations like these that high exposures can occur.

102 If you offer an emergency call-out service, you will need to presume that the work will involve disturbing ACMs so that you or your employees are aware and properly equipped. Err on the side of safety. Follow these simple steps:

◆ where you have an emergency call-out contract with a client, you should either have been made aware in advance of the location of ACMs or have an emergency contact number;

◆ if this cannot be done you should identify the types of emergency work commonly carried out and prepare generic assessments and plans of work which can be used in emergency situations. The assessment will need to detail the types of work which are likely to be carried out and those which must be carried out by a specialist contractor licensed by HSE;

◆ the people carrying out this type of work should be suitably equipped to work with ACMs where this proves necessary;

◆ the people carrying out the work should have sufficient training so that they are aware of what ACM looks like and what it was used for. They should be trained and able to follow the assessment and plan of work safely;

◆ if the people carrying out the work suspect that disturbance of ACMs may be extensive (ie beyond the scope of the generic assessment and equipment), they should not proceed until they have obtained further specialist advice (for example from management, an occupational hygienist or other health and safety professional, the enforcing authority etc).

WARNING WARNING

Emergency call-out work is not an excuse for lower standards.

You or your employees should not attempt work which is beyond the scope of your training and equipment, or which should be carried out by a specialist contractor licensed by HSE. The better trained and equipped you or your employees are, the less likely the work will need to be stopped.

WORKING SAFELY: GENERAL CONSIDERATIONS

103 For the purposes of this guidance, managing the risk from asbestos is normally fairly simple. By following a few simple principles you can ensure that you or your employees are not put at risk while at work. It is important that managers and supervisors (including the self-employed) are aware of the hazards posed by asbestos, the risk presented by the work and the precautions to take.

104 You must also be committed to protecting your health and that of your workers. The death toll from asbestos-related diseases shows the level of suffering which can result from poor management and work practices.

105 This section provides guidance on general principles of control. *Asbestos essentials: Task manual*[1] provides guidance on how these principles can be applied to specific tasks. These can be used to draw up the plan of work.

Figure 45 Work on a fragile asbestos cement roof without proper precautions

OTHER HAZARDS

106 It is important to remember that asbestos may not be the only hazard present. There are many others, some of which have the potential to cause serious injury or death, for example:

◆ heights;

◆ confined spaces;

◆ other hazardous substances;

◆ noise;

◆ electrical equipment;

◆ vehicles.

Figure 46 The consequences of not taking the proper precautions to prevent a fall (staged picture)

107 Figure 45 shows work being carried out on a fragile asbestos cement roof without any precautions against falling either through gaps in the roof where the sheets have been removed, through the roof itself, or off the side of it. There is also no proper means of access. The possible consequences of working in this way are shown in Figure 46. Guidance on safe working at heights is given in *Health and safety in roof work*.[11]

108 The risks presented by these hazards can be significant and often fatal, as described in paragraph 107. You must always take them into account during your risk assessment and write a safe system of work down in the plan of work. This should be followed.

case study

A factory owner was concerned about the condition of the asbestos cement roof on one of his buildings. He asked a 16-year old apprentice to go up and inspect it for damage, lichen growth etc. He kitted him out with overalls, boots, disposable respirator and hard hat. He was well-protected against the very small risk presented by the asbestos fibres present in the roof sheets. Unfortunately, the employer had become fixated on the risk from asbestos and ignored the more immediate and potentially life-threatening risk from working on fragile roofs.

Within 30 minutes the boy had fallen through the roof and was killed.

REMEMBER - CONSIDER ALL RISKS

TRAINING

109 Training should include the following:

◆ the health hazards of asbestos, including the added danger of smoking and working with asbestos;

◆ the presence of other hazards such as working at heights;

◆ the uses and locations of ACMs in buildings and plant;

◆ the type of work you are allowed to do by law;

◆ what the CAW Regulations require you to do;

◆ work methods and equipment;

◆ correct choice, use and maintenance of personal protective equipment;

◆ decontamination procedures;

◆ maintenance of control measures;

◆ emergency procedures;

◆ waste disposal;

◆ where applicable, the role of medical surveillance.

110 Refresher training should be given every year or more often where:

◆ work methods change;

◆ the type of equipment changes;

◆ the type of work changes significantly.

Further information is given in EM2 'Training'.[1]

111 HSE is developing asbestos awareness training material for use in the existing National Vocational Qualification/Scottish Vocational Qualification courses for construction and related

industries. This material is supported by a video which shows the risks of unknowingly disturbing ACMs. Also, HSE and the National Training Organisations of the Construction Forum have jointly produced basic asbestos awareness pocket cards/leaflets which will be distributed to employers and workers in those industries. The training material and the video will be available from HSE Books/HSE Videos. Further information on organisations providing training can be obtained from HSE's InfoLine (Tel: 08701 545500).

AREA PREPARATION

112 Before you begin it may be necessary to prepare the work area. This may involve moving items such as clothes rails in the vicinity of a ceiling tile which needs to be drilled, covering items with polythene sheeting etc. Following the methods given in *Asbestos essentials: Task manual*[1] will minimise fibre release but you will need to take these precautions in case of accidental damage to the ACM.

AREA SEGREGATION

113 Regulation 14 of the CAW Regulations requires that where exposure can exceed an action level the work area should be designated as an 'asbestos area'. It should be designated as a 'respirator zone' if exposure could exceed the control limit (see paragraphs 33-36). These zones should be clearly and separately segregated and warning notices put up (Figure 47). Employees not engaged in the work should not be permitted into either of these designated areas.

114 You may still wish to segregate other areas where work with asbestos is going on.

115 The first aim must be to minimise the release of fibres when carrying out the task. But, there may still be some level of fibre release.

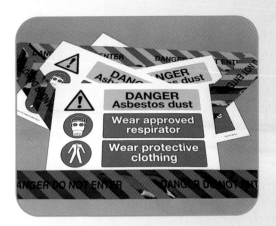

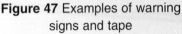

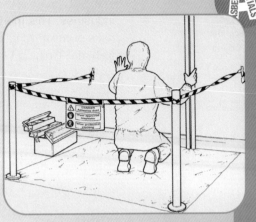

Figure 47 Examples of warning signs and tape

Figure 48 Segregated area

116 How much you need to do will depend on the task and will be decided by the outcome of the assessment. In most cases covered by this guidance, it will be sufficient to divide off the work area, for example using warning tape and signs, to prevent non-asbestos workers approaching (Figure 48).

117 How you segregate the work area will depend on the type of area in which you are working. It may not be appropriate or necessary to erect a barrier and post warning notices in a house, for example when working on a domestic boiler in the kitchen. In this case it may only be necessary to inform the householder that the work is going on and then close the door to that room. What is important is that the person carrying out the work is in control of the work area. However, in a factory environment this may not be as easy. So it may be better to use barriers to restrict access to the work area.

REMEMBER

It is important that you control access to the work area.

118 A physical barrier ('mini enclosure') is required where an AIB ceiling tile is to be removed (see A2, 'Removal of a single asbestos insulating board ceiling tile').[1] Guidance on the design and construction of a 'mini enclosure' is provided in EM3 'Building a "mini enclosure" for the removal of a single asbestos insulating board ceiling tile'.[1] Figure 49 shows a 'mini enclosure' being built for board removal of a ceiling tile.

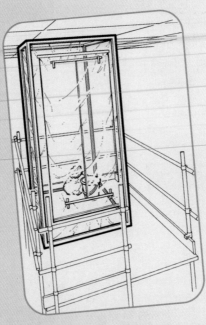

Figure 49 A 'mini enclosure' being built for removal of a ceiling tile

REMEMBER

You must include the time it takes to build and dismantle the enclosure when deciding if the work must be carried out by a specialist contractor licensed by HSE.

119 It is very unlikely that full enclosure with negative pressure units will be necessary for the type of work covered by this guidance. Negative pressure units remove and filter air from an enclosure. This keeps the air pressure inside the enclosure lower than that outside, ensuring that any leaks are inwards. These units are used in major asbestos removal projects by specialist contractors licensed by HSE.

120 The task guidance sheets[1] give advice on the level of segregation required for different tasks.

121 Workers should not eat, drink, or smoke in these areas. Separate arrangements should be made for these activities.

GENERAL GOOD WORK PRACTICES

122 When putting together your plan of work, there are a number of simple measures which can be applied regardless of the task being carried out. These include:

✔ where reasonably practicable, plan the work so that ACMs are not disturbed;

✔ where this is not reasonably practicable, keep disturbance to a minimum;

✔ carry out the work with the minimum number of people present;

✔ make sure surfaces which may get covered in contaminated dust and debris are covered, for example with 500 gauge polythene sheeting;

✔ always work carefully with ACMs;

✔ where practicable, keep the material damp when working on it;

✔ avoid breaking ACMs;

✔ avoid working on ACMs directly above your head;

✔ use hand tools in preference to power or pneumatic tools. Additional control measures such as Local Exhaust Ventilation (LEV) will be needed (see paragraph 124);

✔ where power or pneumatic tools have to be used (sometimes they are preferable, as they take the manual effort out of the task and make it easier to carry it out safely) they should be set at the lowest effective speed and additional control measures used, for example LEV (see paragraph 124);

✘ do not use angle grinders, sanders or grit blasting on ACMs as these will release large amounts of asbestos fibres;

✔ use low dust cleaning methods, such as vacuuming with a Type H (BS 5415) vacuum cleaner, wet rags, impregnated 'Tak Rags' etc (see paragraph 124);

✘ do not use cleaning methods such as sweeping or blowing with compressed air - these will make asbestos fibres airborne where they can be breathed in.

✔ wear suitable personal protective equipment, including respiratory protective equipment (see paragraphs 130-150);

✔ keep the work area clean and tidy;

✔ make sure the work area has been thoroughly cleaned on completion of the work (see paragraphs 155-159);

✔ dispose of asbestos waste correctly (see paragraphs 167-173);

✔ make sure you wash thoroughly each time you leave the work area (see paragraphs 151-154).

123 Specific procedures for individual tasks are given in *Asbestos essentials: Task manual.*[1]

EQUIPMENT AND MATERIALS

124 It is essential that you use or provide your employees with the necessary information, equipment and materials, otherwise the job cannot be carried out safely. The following may be required, although the nature of the job will dictate the specific requirements (see *Asbestos essentials: Task manual*): [1]

◆ *plan of work, task guidance sheets and equipment and method guidance sheets.*[1] These should be available to the people carrying out the work, so that they know and under stand the scope of the work and the precautions to take;

◆ *polythene sheeting, spray adhesive and duct tape* to cover surfaces which may become contaminated. These can also be used where some form of 'mini enclosure' is required. Remember to consider the presence of hazardous substances such as solvents in spray adhesives (see paragraph 85);

◆ *a proprietary 'mini enclosure' or timber or other suitable frame work* to build one (see EM3 'Building a "mini enclosure" for the removal of a single asbestos insulating board ceiling tile');[1]

◆ *warning notices and suitable barriers* to ensure that people who are not involved in the work do not approach (see Figure 47);

◆ *a thick paste,* such as ready-to-use wallpaper paste for drilling materials such as asbestos cement (see Figure 50);

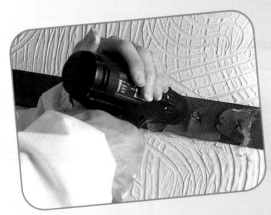

Figure 50 Drilling through paste

◆ *a wetting agent* to help make sure the asbestos fibres are properly wetted (see EM5, 'Wetting asbestos materials');

◆ *a water spray,* for example a garden spray, to keep ACMs damp;

◆ *liquid nails.* This can be used to repair AIB panels. A non-asbestos material can be attached over a hole without the need to be screwed in;

◆ *non-asbestos panelling.* This can be used to protect ACMs from impact;

◆ *a Type H vacuum cleaner (with attachments) to BS5415* (Figure 51). This is a vacuum cleaner fitted with a high efficiency (HEPA) filter which removes very small particles, such as asbestos fibres from the discharged air (see EM4 'Using a Type H vacuum cleaner when working with asbestos').[1] Most domestic type vacuum cleaners do not have HEPA filters and would blow fibres back to the atmosphere. *These and domestic type vacuum cleaners with HEPA filters, but not to BS5415, should not be used;*

High efficiency filter (HEPA)

Figure 51 Schematic diagram of a Type H vacuum cleaner

Cleaning Type H vacuum cleaners can lead to high exposures. This work should be carried out by a specialist company such as a hirer with the necessary facilities and training.

◆ *low speed tools.* Hand tools are preferred, but where power or pneumatic tools need to be used, they should be set at the lowest effective speed. *Tools used for asbestos work should be cleaned each time they are used;*

◆ *hole cutters.* These can be used to cut larger holes in AIB. They can be used with bigger LEV 'enclosures'. The advantage of using these is that part of the hole is removed intact (a disc of AIB will remain in the hole cutter). An ordinary drill will 'destroy' the AIB being cut, creating more dust;

◆ *local exhaust ventilation (LEV).* Measures such as LEV can be used to control fibre release. This can take two forms:

Enclosing the drill point. Plastic 'enclosures' are placed over the point to be drilled and fitted to the Type H (BS5415) vacuum cleaner (Figure 42). The drill is inserted through an opening and the hole drilled. The suction inside the 'enclosure' draws away the dust and asbestos fibres. This can be used for small and large holes. The 'enclosure' should be cleaned after use.

Shadow vacuuming is where the nozzle of a Type H (BS 5415) vacuum cleaner, fitted with a suitable attachment, is held as close as possible to the source of fibre release throughout the task (Figure 52). Shadow vacuuming can be used when using sharp knives, removal of debris, removing screws etc.

Where a Type H (BS 5415) vacuum cleaner is used to provide LEV, it should be checked at the start of each shift; inspected weekly and tested and thoroughly inspected every six months;

Figure 52
Shadow vacuuming during removal of a screw from AIB

◆ *rags.* Household rags, for example cotton (which do not leave fibrous deposits behind) or impregnated rags (for example 'Tak Rags') to remove fine dust deposits and to clean tools such as screw drivers, drill bits, inside of the plastic 'enclosures' etc (see EM7 'Using rags to clean surfaces and equipment contaminated with asbestos');[1]

◆ *a bucket of water* to allow tools etc to be cleaned, rags wetted etc - take care not to get electrical equipment/tools or installations wet;

◆ *sealant.* This will be needed where the work has disturbed ACMs and left unsealed edges or surfaces which need to be repaired. You can also seal ACMs to provide impact resistance or possibly for aesthetic reasons.

In some circumstances, for example, where the ACM is providing thermal insulation or fire protection, the sealant will need to meet the appropriate specification.

There are a number of sealants available. Polymeric elastomers can provide substantial impact resistance for many years. PVA (poly vinyl acetate) can be applied by brush or spray but does not provide much impact resistance. Its main use is the sealing of ACMs such as the backs of ceiling tiles while they are being removed. An alkali-resistant and vapour-permeable sealant is normally required when painting asbestos cement.

Remember to consider hazardous substances which may be present in the sealant (see paragraph 85);

◆ *tools* such as screwdrivers, scrapers, utility knives etc.

◆ *approved asbestos waste containers.* Suitable waste containers should be available for the safe disposal of asbestos waste (see paragraphs 167-173).

◆ *lighting,* so that the person carrying out the work can see properly (work may be carried out in poorly lit areas), particularly to check that the area has been thoroughly cleaned on completion of the work.

◆ *personal protective equipment.* This is dealt with in more detail in paragraphs 130-150.

◆ *smoke tubes.* These can be used to test the integrity of 'mini enclosures'. Figure 53 shows a smoke tube and Figure 54 shows one in use;

Figure 53 Smoke tube

Figure 54 Testing seal with a smoke tube, with second person using a torch to check for smoke leaking from seals

◆ non-asbestos replacement materials. These may be required where ACMs have been removed (see paragraphs 42-45).

WHERE CAN YOU BUY OR HIRE THIS EQUIPMENT?

125 A lot of the equipment described in paragraph 124 can be obtained from good hardware or hire shops. Details of where to get the more specialised equipment can be obtained from the organisations listed on page v.

WHAT DO YOU DO IF ACMS ARE FOUND OR ACCIDENTALLY DISTURBED?

126 It is possible that, even after every precaution has been taken, you may come across 'hidden' ACMs when working in a building or on plant. It is important that you know what they look like and what you should do.

127 It is also possible that ACMs you are working on or nearby could be damaged. Again, you need to know what to do.

128 Figure 55 outlines a suggested course of action.

Figure 55 One course of action you can take if you realise that you may be working on ACMs that you had not been warned about, or they are accidently damaged during the job.

STOP WORK IMMEDIATELY

Prevent anyone entering the area

Have you any dust or debris on yourself or your clothing?

YES

Remove clothing and place in a plastic bag

If possible take a shower, otherwise wash thoroughly

Make sure the washing facilities are left in a clean condition

NO

Report the problem to the person in charge as soon as possible

The work can be carried out by someone without a licence from HSE

Assess the job and use the task guidance sheets and the information in paragraphs 103-173 to develop a safe system of work

Arrange for a sample of the material to be taken for analysis

NO

Is the material asbestos lagging, coating or AIB?

NO

Will the clean up work take more than one hour per worker or two hours in total (total work in seven consecutive days)?

Employ a specialist contractor licenced by HSE

Does it contain asbestos?

YES

YES

YES

NO

NO ACTION REQUIRED

59

Waste handling

129   It is important that waste material is handled carefully, otherwise you could be exposed to asbestos fibres or have a spillage of asbestos debris. You should:

✔ double bag the waste. You can place the asbestos waste bag (paragraph 170) inside a clear bag so that it is obvious they are double bagged (see Figure 56);

Figure 56 Asbestos waste double bagged

✔ seal the waste bag by twisting the end tightly and then wrapping with duct tape;

✘ not overfill the waste bag. This makes it difficult to seal and carry;

✘ avoid expelling air from the bag before sealing it. The air will be contaminated with asbestos fibres;

✔ wipe clean the inner bag before double bagging and the outer one before removal from the work area;

✘ never break ACMs to fit them in a waste bag - wrap them in 1000 gauge polythene sheeting and label that instead. Figure 57 shows a door with an AIB panel wrapped in polythene sheeting;

✔ wrap any sharp materials, which could puncture a bag, in 1000 gauge polythene sheeting, and label it. If the sheeting is wrapped loosely around the object it is less likely to puncture it;

✔ waste bags should be handled with care - do not throw them.

Figure 57 Door with an AIB panel wrapped in polythene sheeting

PROTECTIVE CLOTHING

130 When someone is working with ACMs their clothing may collect dust and debris. For this reason, it is advisable to provide them with protective clothing, such as footwear and disposable overalls.

131 You should use boots without laces, for example wellingtons, as they are easier to clean.

132 Disposable overalls are normally better than cotton overalls, as they don't need to be laundered. Cotton, or other types of overalls, can be worn during the remainder of the work when ACMs are not being disturbed.

133 In some circumstances you will need to consider other types of protective clothing, for example working outside in cold and wet conditions may require waterproof clothing to be worn.

134 It is important that overalls are worn correctly, for example:

✔ it is normally advisable to wear a size too big. This helps prevent them from ripping at the seams if you stretch;

✔ if the cuffs are loose, tape them to prevent any dust getting into the sleeve;

✘ avoid long sleeve shirts which may be difficult to cover;

✔ the legs should be worn over footwear, for example, they should not be tucked into wellington boots as dust can get into the tops;

✔ the hood should be over the straps on the RPE (this should cover the fringe of your hair);

✘ do not wear the hood under the straps as this can result in the RPE 'moving' slightly as the hood moves with the actions of the wearer. If you are wearing the hood as shown in Figure 58, you are wearing it correctly.

135 Protective clothing should be cleaned before removal. If the task guidance sheets[1] have been followed, the amount of cleaning should be minimal. In most cases it will be sufficient to use a wet rag to pat clean the overalls. But, where a Type H (BS5415) vacuum cleaner is available it can be used instead. Where there are two of you working together you can each clean the other's overalls - this makes it easier to clean areas such as the back of your shoulders.

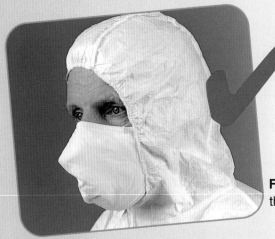

Figure 58 Hood worn over the RPE - correct

136 The protective clothing should be cleaned and removed when leaving the work area for breaks and at the end of the job. The best way of removing overalls is to turn them inside out as they are being taken off. This minimises contact with the outer surface of the clothing. They can then be placed in an asbestos waste container. Leave your RPE on until you have removed and

bagged your overalls. Further information can be found in EM8 'Personal decontamination'.[1]

137 Protective clothing should be stored separately from clean clothing. Used overalls should *never* be taken home. If you use cotton overalls you will need to make arrangements for cleaning at a specialised laundry equipped to deal with asbestos-contaminated clothing and follow their packaging procedures. Waterproof clothing will need to be sponged or wiped clean.

RESPIRATORY PROTECTIVE EQUIPMENT (RPE)

138 RPE should not be used as the only means of controlling exposure. Before considering the use of RPE, the amount of asbestos fibres in the air should be reduced as low as is reasonably practicable by other means, such as those described in this guidance and the *Asbestos essentials: Task manual.*[1]

139 If, despite these precautions, exposure to asbestos fibres is likely to exceed the control limit, then you must always provide suitable RPE (in addition to the other precautions) which should then reduce exposure as low as reasonably practicable and in any case below the control limit. If you follow the methods given in the task guidance sheets[1] it is unlikely that the control limits will be exceeded. However, it is recommended that RPE still be used as an added precaution.

140 Different types of RPE have different efficiencies. Always remember to choose RPE which protects employees from a level of exposure well within the upper limit of its protection range. If in doubt, always select higher performance equipment, providing that it is suitable for the task.

141 It is very important that the most suitable type of RPE is chosen and that it is worn correctly. Otherwise, you or your employees will not be protected from asbestos fibres while carrying out the task.

142 The effectiveness of RPE depends on a good fit between the wearer's skin and the face seal of the mask. Otherwise, air containing asbestos fibres will pass between the RPE and the wearers' face without being filtered (Figure 59). The selection of RPE should therefore include quantitative or qualitative fit testing.

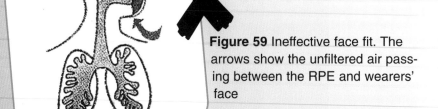

Figure 59 Ineffective face fit. The arrows show the unfiltered air passing between the RPE and wearers' face

143 Quantative and qualitative fit testing applies to whatever type of RPE is being worn and is a method of making sure that the wearer chooses RPE which is the best fit possible. There are several methods by which this test can be carried out. Your supplier will be able to advise you.

144 The task guidance sheets[1] indicate the type of RPE which can be used. For the purposes of the maintenance work covered by this guidance a disposable particulate respirator (FFP3) will be adequate. *But, when assessing the job you should ensure that the RPE will provide sufficient protection and is suitable for the task.*

145 Figure 60 shows one example of the wrong type of disposable respirator used on a task involving work with asbestos. This picture shows a general 'nuisance dust' respirator. It has been 'doubled-up' in an attempt to provide better protection.

Figure 60: The wrong type of RPE for use with asbestos ('nuisance dust' respirator) doubled up to 'try' and give more protection

146 Figure 61 again shows the wrong type of disposable respirator ('nuisance dust'). This has been 'screwed up' and kept in the worker's pocket during a break. Even if it were the correct type it would be difficult to wear it properly.

REMEMBER

You should never rely on RPE as your main method of controlling exposure.

RPE is no substitute for minimising the quantity of fibres released.

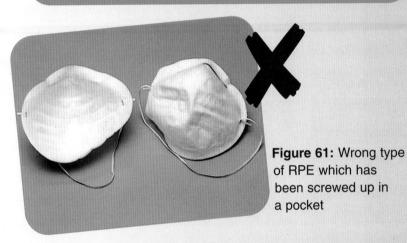

Figure 61: Wrong type of RPE which has been screwed up in a pocket

147 Figure 62 shows RPE being worn in the wrong way:

◆ the bottom strap is not around the wearer's head;

◆ the top has not been 'pinched' against the wearer's nose - a gap is clearly visible;

◆ the hood is down.

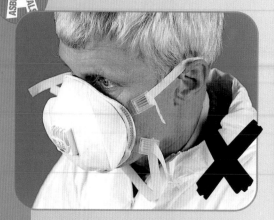

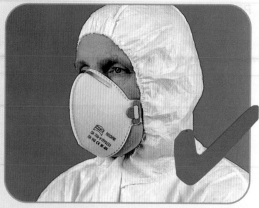

Figure 62 Disposable RPE being worn wrongly

Figure 63: If your disposable RPE looks like this then you are wearing it correctly

148 If your disposable RPE fits like the example given in Figure 63, you are wearing it correctly.

149 To fit properly:

✔ the wearer should be clean shaven;

✔ both straps should be placed firmly around the top/back of the head;

✔ the top should be 'pinched' over the nose;

✔ spectacle wearers should take their spectacles off before putting RPE on, otherwise the face piece can sit on the frame, causing a gap. The RPE should be fitted and then the spectacles put on;

✔ the hood should be worn over the RPE straps.

150 Further guidance on the correct choice and use of RPE can be found in:

◆ EM6 'Personal protective equipment';[1]

◆ the free HSE leaflet *Selection of suitable respiratory protective equipment for work with asbestos.*[12]

PROVISION OF CLEANING AND HYGIENE FACILITIES

151 Hygiene facilities will need to be provided so that you or your employees can wash thoroughly after working with ACMs. The type and extent of the washing facilities will depend on the nature and degree of exposure to asbestos.

152 If you follow the task guidance sheets,[1] exposure should be low. It will normally be possible for you to use the existing washing facilities where you are working. As a precaution, access to these facilities will need to be limited to the workers involved in the asbestos work.

153 But, If you do not decontaminate yourself properly, you may take asbestos fibres home on your clothing. You or your family and friends could be exposed to them if they were disturbed and became airborne. Further information can be found in EM8 'Personal decontamination'.[1]

154 Once the work has finished the facilities should be cleaned and inspected (see paragraphs 155-159). If the work lasts for several days, then they should be cleaned and inspected daily.

CLEARANCE TESTING

155 Once the work is finished it is important that the work area is checked to make sure that it can be safely reoccupied. This process can be split into two parts:

◆ a visual inspection;

◆ air monitoring;

Together, this is referred to as 'clearance testing'.

156 The most important part is the visual inspection. This is a detailed check of all surfaces within the segregated area/enclosure (and any other area which may have become contaminated, for example washing facilities). The aim is to make sure that all traces of asbestos (except for any material that is supposed to remain) and other dust and debris have been removed.

157 It is important to remove all dust deposits, even if they do not immediately look like asbestos. This is because they may have become contaminated with microscopic fibres which are not visible to the naked eye. The inspection should also include any asbestos-containing materials remaining in the area to make sure that they have been properly sealed or protected.

158 Figure 64 is a picture taken by a microscope of ordinary dust containing microscopic asbestos fibres. If the dust were disturbed these would become airborne and could be breathed in. This shows why it is important that you carefully clean all dust from surfaces which may have been contaminated.

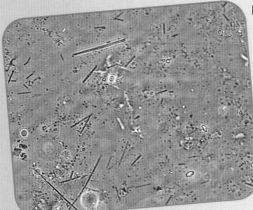

Figure 64: Microscopic (x 400 magnification) asbestos fibres (dark needle-like structures) in dust from a surface which was not cleaned properly following asbestos removal - these would not be visible to the naked eye. The dark specks and light needle-like structures are non-asbestos dust

159 In major asbestos removal jobs the visual inspection is normally followed by air monitoring. This makes sure that any remaining asbestos fibres in the air are below permitted levels. If the task guidance sheets[1] are followed carefully, it will not normally be necessary to carry out air monitoring for the types of tasks covered by this guidance.

AIR MONITORING

160 If you carry out the tasks using this guidance then you should be able to prevent or control exposure to a level as low as reasonably practicable. Therefore, air monitoring will *not normally* be required.

161 However, you may wish to consider air monitoring:

◆ as confirmation that you are adequately controlling the exposure;

◆ where the work is of a particularly sensitive nature to the building occupants. In such cases it can be used to reassure them that all is well;

◆ to provide proof of control to an inspector.

162 Figure 65 shows someone wearing personal monitoring equipment correctly. This consists of a sampling pump, worn on the worker's belt, attached by a length of plastic tubing to a sampling head on his lapel. The sampling pump draws air at a known rate over a filter held in the sampling head. The filter is analysed using a microscope.

163 If the equipment is worn or used incorrectly, you will get a false measure of exposure.

Figure 65: Personal monitoring equipment worn correctly

164 As an employer you must only use laboratories to carry out air monitoring who can demonstrate that they conform to European Standard EN45001 by accreditation with a recognised accreditation body. As part of this, these laboratories will need to demonstrate satisfactory performance in a quality assurance scheme known as RICE (Regular Inter-laboratory Counting

Exchanges). This scheme monitors the performance of laboratories who carry out the analysis of measurements of asbestos fibres in air. A list of accredited laboratories can be obtained from the United Kingdom Accreditation Service (UKAS) (Tel: 020 8917 8400).

165 If you wish to carry out your own air monitoring, you must make sure that employees carrying out the monitoring receive similar standards of training, supervision and quality control to those required by EN45001.

166 Further guidance on air monitoring is given in *Asbestos: exposure limits and measurements of airborne dust concentrations*[13] and *Asbestos fibres in air.*[14]

WASTE DISPOSAL

167 Asbestos waste, defined as any waste containing more than 0.1% w/w (weight for weight) asbestos in the waste, is subject to the waste management controls set out in the Special Waste Regulations 1996 (as amended) and must be consigned to a site which is authorised to accept asbestos waste. This is enforced by the Environment Agency in England and Wales, and the Scottish Environment Protection Agency in Scotland.

168 The Special Waste Regulations 1996 place duties on:

◆ consignors (the company causing the waste to be removed);

◆ carriers (the waste collector); and

◆ consignees (the waste management facility).

169 The consignor must ensure that the relevant special waste consignment note is completed and signed. Details must include:

◆ an accurate waste description;

◆ the total quantity;

◆ the total number and weight (or volume) of each package;

◆ a hazard code;

◆ the process giving rise to the waste.

170 Whatever type of waste container (for example, a plastic sack) is used it should be:

◆ made of a material which in normal handling is strong enough to contain the waste and which takes account, if necessary, of materials in the waste sharp enough to cause punctures;

◆ capable of being readily decontaminated before leaving the work area;

◆ kept secure on site until sent for disposal, for example in a locked skip;

◆ properly labelled (see Figure 66).

171 In certain circumstances the following Regulations may apply to the waste material:

◆ The Carriage of Dangerous Goods (Classification, Packaging and Labelling) and The Transportable Pressure Receptacles Regulations 1996;

◆ The Carriage of Dangerous Goods by Road Regulations 1996;

◆ The Carriage of Dangerous Goods by Rail Regulations 1996;

◆ The Carriage of Dangerous Goods by Road (Driver Training) Regulations 1996;

◆ The Transport of Dangerous Goods (Safety Advisers) Regulations 1999.

Where these Regulations do not apply, Schedule 2 of the CAW Regulations will be applicable.

172 Further guidance can be found in:

◆ *Carriage of dangerous goods explained. Guidance for consignors of dangerous goods by road and rail (classification, packaging and provision of information). Part 1;*[15]

◆ *Carriage of dangerous goods explained. Guidance for road vehicle operators and others involved in the carriage of dangerous goods by road. Part 2.*[16]

◆ *Carriage of dangerous goods explained. Guidance for rail operators and others involved in the carriage of dangerous goods by rail. Part 3.*[17]

◆ *The Transport of Dangerous Goods (Safety Advisers) Regulations 1999.*[18]

◆ *Dangerous Goods Safety Advisers.*[19]

◆ *Are you involved in the carriage of dangerous goods by road or rail?*[20]

> **REMEMBER**
>
> Illegal dumping of asbestos waste is punishable by the Courts.

173 Further information can be obtained from the Environment Agency (Enquiry Line: 08459 333111) in England and Wales and the Scottish Environment Protection Agency in Scotland (Head Office: 01786 457700) and see Figure 67.

Figure 66: Labelling requirements for plastic bags/sacks containing asbestos waste

Proper shipping name	Class number	
Waste blue asbestos (crocidolite)	UN 2212	Carriage of Dangerous Goods (Classification, Packaging and Labelling) and Use of Transportable Pressure Receptacles Regulations 1996 Regulations 7 and 8 refer
Waste brown asbestos (amosite)	UN 2212	
Waste white asbestos (chrysotile)	UN 2590	

Danger sign

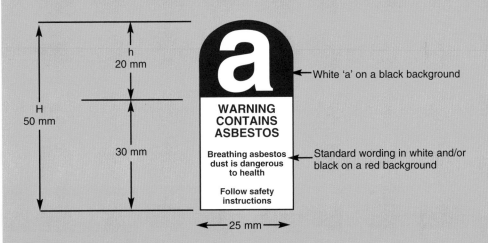

The dimensions in millilitres of the label shall be those shown on the diagram, except that larger measurements may be used, but in that case the dimension of the label indicated as h, on the diagram above, shall be 40% of the dimension indicated as H on that diagram.

The label shall be clearly and indelibly printed so that the words in the lower half of the label can be easily read, and those words shall be printed in black or white.

Figure 67: Procedure for dealing with asbestos waste

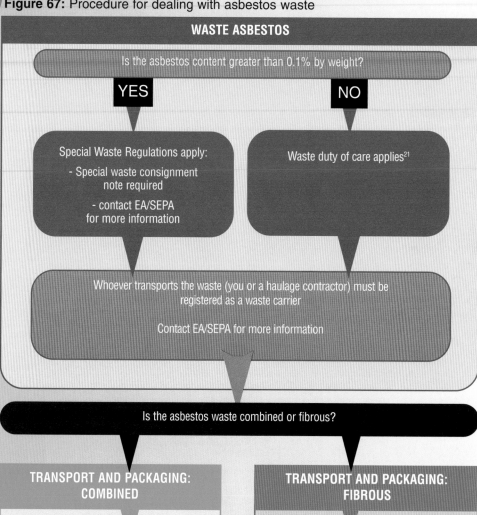

WASTE ASBESTOS

Is the asbestos content greater than 0.1% by weight?

YES

NO

Special Waste Regulations apply:
- Special waste consignment note required
- contact EA/SEPA for more information

Waste duty of care applies[21]

Whoever transports the waste (you or a haulage contractor) must be registered as a waste carrier

Contact EA/SEPA for more information

Is the asbestos waste combined or fibrous?

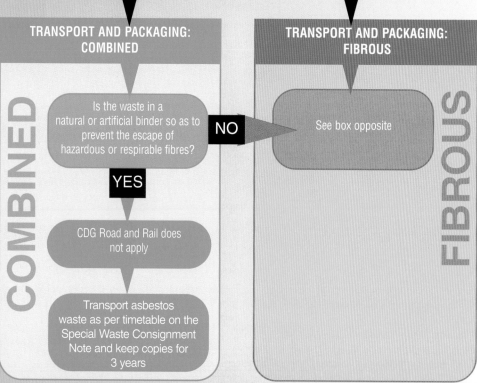

TRANSPORT AND PACKAGING: COMBINED

TRANSPORT AND PACKAGING: FIBROUS

COMBINED

FIBROUS

Is the waste in a natural or artificial binder so as to prevent the escape of hazardous or respirable fibres?

NO

See box opposite

YES

CDG Road and Rail does not apply

Transport asbestos waste as per timetable on the Special Waste Consignment Note and keep copies for 3 years

FIBROUS

The waste is dangerous for transport, CDG Road and Rail applies

Asbestos cannot be transported in bulk, it must be packed in UN approved packages displaying:

- Proper shipping name
- Class number
- Danger sign (see Figure 66)

Does the vehicle in which the waste is to be transported have a maximum weight in excess of 3.5 tons?

YES

- Driver to be trained for Class 9 Dangerous Goods

- Vehicle to be fitted with a 2 kg dry powder extinguisher in cab (>3.5 tonnes - 6 kg)

- Emergency information (Tremcard) to be provided to the driver

NO

Does the Weight of the asbestos exceed:
- Blue or brown - 200g ?
- White - 500g ?

YES

Are the packages of asbestos to be carried in a vehicle or in a bulk container on a vehicle?

NO

Bulk container | **Vehicle**

- Vehicle to display **orange panel** at front and rear
- Danger signs to be displayed on at least one side of the bulk container

Vehicle to display **orange panel** at front and rear

Transport as per timetable on the Special Waste Consignment Note

Special Waste Consignment Note to be kept by the consignor for three years.
Other documentation to be kept by the operator for three months.

Key
EA: Environment Agency
SEPA: Scottish Environment Protection Agency
CDG Road and Rail: five sets of regulations (see list in paragraph 171)

TASK GUIDANCE AND EQUIPMENT AND METHOD GUIDANCE SHEETS

174   The task guidance sheets give practical guidance on how 25 common tasks can be safely carried out. If you closely follow the method given in the sheets you will be able to prevent or reduce exposure to asbestos fibres to a level as low as reasonably practicable.

175   The task guidance sheets refer to the range of equipment and methods which should be followed so as to make sure that the procedure is effective. If the wrong equipment is used, or used in the wrong way, you will not get the full benefit.

176   The equipment and method guidance sheets describe the equipment and how to use it. The task guidance sheets tell you when particular equipment and method guidance sheets should be consulted.

177   You can use these sheets, along with the information provided in paragraphs 103-173 when preparing a safe system of work and plan of work. It is strongly recommended that workers are given copies of *Asbestos essentials: Task manual*[1] as part of the plan of work. They can use the task guidance sheets to make sure they are doing the job properly.

178   It is important that a task guidance sheet is only used for the task it is meant for, for example, the task guidance sheet for repairing AC is not appropriate if you are working on AIB - you would not effectively control exposure.

179   The photographs in each task guidance sheet and equipment and method guidance sheet[1] illustrate how the task should be done or what it should look like when completed. For illustrative purposes, many of the illustrations show the task being carried out on non-ACMs.

REFERENCES

1   *Asbestos essentials: Task manual* HSG210 2000 HSE Books
    ISBN 0 7176 1887 0

2   Peto J, Hodgson J 'Continuing increase in mesothelioma
    mortality in Britain' *The Lancet* 1995 **345** (8949) 535-539

3   *Working with asbestos cement* HSG189/2 1999 HSE Books
    ISBN 0 7176 1667 3

4   *Control of asbestos at work* L27 1999 HSE Books
    ISBN 0 7176 1673 8

5   *Guide to the Asbestos (Licensing) Regulations* L11 1999
    HSE Books ISBN 0 7176 2435 8

6   *Managing construction for health and safety: Construction
    (Design and Management) Regulations 1994. Approved Code
    of Practice* L54 1995 HSE Books ISBN 0 7176 0792 5

7   *A guide to the Construction (Health, Safety and Welfare)
    Regulations 1996* Leaflet INDG220 1996 HSE Books (single
    copy free or priced packs of 10 ISBN 0 7176 1161 2)

8   *Surveying, sampling and assessment of asbestos-containing
    materials* MDHS100 2001 HSE Books ISBN 0 7176 2076 X

9   *COSHH: A brief guide to the Regulations: What you need to
    know about the Control of Substances Hazardous to Health
    Regulations 1999 (COSHH)* Leaflet INDG136(rev1) 1999
    HSE Books (single copy free or priced packs of 10
    ISBN 0 7176 2444 7)

10 *Management of health and safety at work. Management of
    Health and Safety at Work Regulations 1999. Approved Code
    of Practice and guidance* L21 2000 HSE Books
    ISBN 0 7176 2488 9

11 *Health and safety in roof work* HSG33 (Second edition) 1998
    HSE Books ISBN 0 7176 1425 5

12 *Selection of suitable respiratory protective equipment for work
    with asbestos* Leaflet INDG288 1999 HSE Books (single copy
    free or priced packs of 5 ISBN 0 7176 2456 0)

13   *Asbestos: Exposure limits and measurements of airborne dust concentrations* EH10 2001 HSE Books ISBN 0 7176 2129 4

14   *Asbestos fibres in air* MDHS 39/4 1995 HSE Books ISBN 0 7176 1113 2

15   *Carriage of dangerous goods explained. Guidance for consignors of dangerous goods by road and rail (classification, labelling and provision of information). Part 1* HSG160 1996 HSE Books ISBN 0 7176 1255 4

16   *Carriage of dangerous goods explained. Guidance for road vehicle operators and others involved in the carriage of dangerous goods by road. Part 2* HSG161 1996 HSE Books ISBN 0 7176 1253 8

17   *Carriage of dangerous goods explained. Guidance for rail operators and others involved in the carriage of dangerous goods by rail. Part 3* HSG163 1996 HSE Books ISBN 0 7176 1256 2

18   *The Transport of Dangerous Goods (Safety Advisers) Regulations 1999* SI 1999/257 1999 TSO ISBN 0 11 080434 1

19   *Dangerous Goods Safety Advisers* AO677 DETR and Scottish Qualifications Authority

20   *Are you involved in the carriage of dangerous goods by road or rail* Leaflet INDG234(rev) 1999 HSE Books (single copy free or priced packs of 10 ISBN 0 7176 1676 2)

21   *Waste Management. The duty of care. A code of practice. Environment Protection Act 1990, Section 34* 1996 HMSO ISBN 0 11 753210 X

While every effort has been made to ensure the accuracy of the references listed in this publication, their future availability cannot be guaranteed.

Printed and published by the Health and Safety Executive   C100   10/01